Class Action

written and illustrated by
John Patrick Green

with colour by **Wes Dzioba**

MACMILLAN CHILDREN'S BOOKS

For principles and principals

First published in the US 2024 by First Second

First published in the UK 2024 by Macmillan Children's Books
an imprint of Pan Macmillan
The Smithson, 6 Briset Street, London EC1M 5NR
EU representative: Macmillan Publishers Ireland Ltd, 1st Floor,
The Liffey Trust Centre, 117–126 Sheriff Street Upper
Dublin 1, D01 YC43
Associated companies throughout the world
www.panmacmillan.com

ISBN 978-1-0350-1543-6

1 3 5 7 9 8 6 4 2

A CIP catalogue record for this book is available from the British Library.

Cover design by John Patrick Green and Kirk Benshoff
Interior book design by John Patrick Green
Colour by Wes Dzioba

Printed in China

Chapter 1

The city Botanical Garden.

Things are pretty green here.

Even MORE green than usual!

STOP, THIEF!

These **sunflowers** are the final component I, the **FLORA-FIEND,** need to harness enough SOLAR ENERGY to power my ecologically conscious **DESTRUCTO-RAY!**
(Patent pending.)

Those flowers are property of the city **Botanical Garden!**

You'll never catch me!

EXHIBIT WORLD'S RAREST FLORA

This botany bandit won't get far!

?!

HOIST!

Nice job, **Mango!**

Thanks, **Brash!**

Another villain foiled, thanks to the—

MA
FERTILI

4

Armando's and don'ts! Are you *TOO STINKY* to enter S.U.I.T. HQ even *AFTER* a trip through the sewers? Then Arman-***don't!*** Instead, Arman-***do*** L.A.U.N.D.R.Y.!

Lavatory

TOO stinky?

You do still REEK of that **funky flower**, Mango. This code must be for a—

Sniff Sni,—

Lavatory ...es to the ...derground

What—?! *WAIT!* Mango was the one who—

HA HA!

NAB!

GRAB!

≥Urk.!∈

12

You got a stinky smell up and down, all around,
STAIN REMOVAL
spritz
spritz
Oh! L.A.U.N.D.R.Y. must be the new decontamination procedure, Brash!
There's a whole lot of cleanin' to do now!
DEEP SCRUB
GLORP!
Yes, Mango, that much I've gathered!
SCRUB
GURBLE BURBLE
SCRUB
SCRUB

We don't want the funk! Get rid of your funk!
PSSH
SPIN CYCLE
PSSH
!
WHIRL!
Refreshing!
OWW, can't have that funk! Your funk is bunk!
HOT PRESS
Toasty!
FSSSSSSSS
Why do I get the feeling we're the only agents who have to go through this?

*Digital Ocular Remote Butler

G.I. Moe can't even change his **password** without Monocle's help.

He can probably find his way out of a **robe**, though.

Ready, Brash? On three . . .

FLASH

. . . THREE!

YEESH! Thanks for the warning.

Agent Brash! There you are.

Hmm?

*Computerized Ocular Remote Butler

They look accurate to **me**. And the General Inspector's photo turned out fine.

HEY, you never said there was a **laser beam** background option! I got the plain ol' bookcase.

THE G.I. DOESN'T HAVE A **SNOUT** LIKE ME AND BRASH!

Well, *sorry*. I'm just ONE eyeball. I don't have any DEPTH PERCEPTION!

If only there were MORE D-ORBS. You coulda had **3D** photos!

dink doink

Rip Shred Tear Shred Tear Rip Tear Rip Shred

Ooh, confetti!

We have our mission, Mango! Now to see **SVEN SEPTAPUS** and get new V.E.S.T.*s!

WAIT, BRASH! I missed all the important bits! The *what!* The *why!* The *WHERE!*

You've got to start paying more **ATTENTION,** Mango!

Baa-bye!

*Very Exciting Spy Technology

23

Chapter 3

And *your* name is **Brain?** Why don't I get to be the smart one?

That says **BRIAN,** not BRAIN.

Honestly, I think we need to get your eyes and ears checked, Mango. *I mean,* **Martin.**

Martin and Brian, may I present to you . . .

. . . your new V.E.S.T.s! Now, juvenile fashion changes at an *ALARMING* rate, so these **outfits** will be **out of style** by the time you get to recess.

And to give you a more *youthful* profile, I had to strip these of the *larger* detective gear.

That's why I've come up with **B.A.C.K.packs:**

flip

turn

The **B**odily **A**ppliance **C**ontraption...for **K**ids!

They're PACKED with gadgets, so if any kid gets *suspicious* of you, you'll have a plethora of **distractions** at your disposal.

Beep

Plethora?

OOH!

I **LOVE** these fidgety spin thingies!

I grew up in these suburbs, ya know. Well, for the most part.

You're not done growing yet! We're youthful SCHOOLKIDS, remember?

And did you say our mission is to protect a school mascot?

Odd, right? We've saved WORLD LEADERS...SCIENTISTS... even **RENOWNED PASTRY CHEFS!**

A **foam costume** doesn't exactly rise to the same level of *national importance.*

Chapter 4

Shortly...

This is it, Mango.

Hurry! We're gonna miss the beginning of first period!

SQUEEZE

Where...where are we now?

Hold on...P.S. 366?

No way! I *went* to this school!

PUBLIC SCHOOL 366

OH, but wait! The **GYM TEACHER** is probably the coach for the sports teams.

They might know why the **mascot** is in danger.

And I've got . . . CHEMISTRY?

≋SIGH≋

Well, with luck *THIS* teacher won't be as tough as **Ms Burrowbridge** was. I'd like to do better than a C+ this time!

Focus on the MISSION, Mango.

Don't worry about **passing grades.**

Worry about **passing** for a *student!*

41

Chapter 5

So THAT'S what that rumbling is.

It's a **free-for-all!**

A veritable *Lord of the Flies!*

Unsuspecting fidget spinner...

...or clever **SPY DRONE?** Heh heh...

...since the ones at all the *OTHER* schools have gone missing, it's safer if *I* wear it instead of a student.

YES, it'll fit! Don't worry. This gives us an even *better* shot at the championship. *GO BUCKS!*

I mean, **BUCKY** isn't going anywhere.

Our mascot will be locked up *NICE AND TIGHT* until tomorrow...

MASCOT STORAGE

click

...and I've got the *only key!*

...and I've got the *only key!*

RAD'S

Meanwhile...

These halls sure bring back memories.

Some good, some... not so much.

Stay Classy! (Go to class!)

LAB

Hm? Oh, nice!

The teacher isn't here to scold me for showing up late.

49

Hurr hurr . . .

DUNK

Check it out, **Martian.**

Now she's got a PURPLE PIGTAIL!

≥Grumble≤ . . . Same school, new tormentors.

≥AHEM.!≤

What? I didn't do anything.

Oh, really?

Her hair fell into that by **accident.**

Martian saw it, *didn't you?* Tell her. Tell her it was an accident.

I don't need his calculator to put two and two together.

TELL. HER.

Chapter 6

BBRRING

Martin!

MARTIN!

Oh, hey, Bra— Brian. How was gym?

The coach has **Bucky** under lock and key. And with **us** on the premises, that **mascot costume** is as protected as it's gonna get.

Still, that doesn't mean we should let our guard down.

ANYONE could have it out for that deer.

Deer? Deer who?

The mascot. I assume it's a **DEER** because the school team is the **BUCKS.** Right?

GO BUCKS!
P.S.366

Huh? No, the mascot is an **EGG.** Bucky's a big egg costume.

BUCKY

≥AHEM!≤

What? I didn't do anything.

Oh, really?

Her hair fell into that by **accident.**

Martian saw it, *didn't you?* Tell her. Tell her it was an accident.

I don't need his calculator to put two and two together.

TELL. HER.

'The Bucks get CLUCKY against the Easttown Eagles.'

'Bucks EGGcel opposite Redwood Rhinos.'

'Fairville Foxes find Bucks tough eggs to crack!'

'Teal City Tigers had Bucks scrambling for a win.'

Hang on — I overheard the coach say 'the ones at all the OTHER schools have gone missing' . . .

Other MASCOTS?

We may have uncovered a **conspiracy** to steal the mascot costumes of *every school* in the tristate area!

≥GASP!≤

A coordinated plot like that would be hard to keep under wraps! There's gotta be a **teacher** or **student** here who's heard a rumour through the grape juice.

Grapevine.

That, too.

We need people to start talking, and quickly!

BRING

I'LL look into the school faculty, and YOU get popular with the kids.

P-popular...?

It's the only way they'll let you into their *inner circle*.

See you at lunch!

I was *never* good at making friends in school.

I don't know how to be **popular.**

Popular. Pop-u-lar ... That's a weird word.

Isn't it also a tree? No, that's **POPLAR.**

Are **poplar** trees **popular** trees?

ACK!

Speaking of *trees,* I gotta *LEAVE* for maths class!

Chapter 7

Lunchtime...

Wow, the last two periods just *FLEW BY!*

Class doesn't feel as **long** as it did when I was a kid.

School **pizza** is the same as I remember...

...*ABSOLUTELY DELICIOUS.*

BRYAN! *I mean,* BRIAN! Over here!

I wonder who the coach was on the phone with. So far he's been my most **suspicious teacher.**

Now that you mention it, something seemed off with my chemistry substitute. **Ms Foxworth.**

Off how?

She *smiled* the whole time!

That's not natural for a teacher, right? **Ms Burrowbridge** would constantly *FROWN* at me!

I used to call her Ms **FURROW**bridge.

You'd do better if you weren't always doodling in class, Mango.

Hopefully somebody in our *NEXT* classes will know something. I've had **gym**, **art** and **music**. After lunch I've got **shop class**, then **home economics**.

CHEESE AND CARROTS, *Brian!*

You want some?

How come YOU get all the FUN classes? I had **science**, **maths** and **geography**, and next I have **English** and **history!**

It feels like *I'M* in **REAL SCHOOL** and *YOU'RE* in **SUMMERY CAMP!**

The SUMMARY so far is, we're here to stop a **mascot thief** from stealing Bucky before the big **PEP RALLY.**

Which according to this flyer is *TOMORROW!*

Aw, if it's anything like they used to be, the pep rally will be AWESOME!

Some kid'll come out in the Bucky costume, do a whole routine and *TOTALLY HYPE* everyone up!

Eh, we'll see. **Coach** is wearing the costume this year.

That *WILL* be somethin' to see.

Ya know, Brian ...P.S. 366 has the most to *GAIN* from those other school mascots going missing and us making sure Bucky *DOESN'T.*

Without their mascots, the players on *those* teams will be **DEMORALIZED.**

Which will make them easier to beat.

Is **SCHOOL SPIRIT** really *THAT* effective? Besides, with a giraffe on this team, the Bucks have *enough* of a **leg up.**

Don't you mean **NECK** up?

Exactly! The Bucks have an **advantage** because of that giraffe's height.

Technically, in basketball, *WINGSPAN* gives a greater **edge** than *height.*

And last I checked, giraffes don't have wings.

Really? *Hmm* . . . You could be onto something . . .

COULD be? Buddy, I am *pretty sure* giraffes do **not** have wings.

RAD

Maybe . . . an overzealous Bucks fan with *TOO MUCH* **school spirit** stole the *OTHER* school mascots to give *THIS* team an advantage on the court.

RAD

COOL BEANS

S.U.I.T.

If that's **TRUE** . . . then *THIS* school's mascot suit isn't in any ACTUAL danger. And it doesn't explain how this case relates to suit security. *I mean, S.U.I.T. security.*

We shouldn't rule out that someone really *IS* after **Bucky.** But *something* about this isn't adding up.

Would you like my calculator?

zip

bip

This might be thinking outside the box a little, but ... could someone with **internal access** to S.U.I.T. have *manipulated* the G.I. into sending us here?

If so, that would mean ... there's a **mole** in S.U.I.T.!

≷GASP!≷ A **MOLE!** A *spy* among *spies!*

That must be why G.I. Moe's a desperado.

INCOMMUNICADO.

Right!

'The General Inspector's mission brief *DID* say the security of S.U.I.T. hangs in the balance.'

'If there *IS* a **mole,** then our entire investigation could be compromised!'

'Let's just hope this *theoretical* mole doesn't know our *real* identities.'

What's this . . . ?

Mango and Brash?

Detective . . . **FROGS?**

Chapter 8

Did you ever perform as the mascot when you went here?

I tried out for it once.

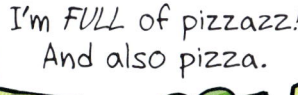

They said my routine lacked focus. That it had no **pizzazz.** I've got *plenty* of pizzazz.

I'm *FULL* of pizzazz! And also pizza.

Mostly I just couldn't see a thing in that egg.

Oh, hey! There's my old locker.

I wonder if my combination still works . . .

STOP! You don't know whose locker that is now!

That's an invasion of privacy. We may be **UNDER**cover, but we're not **ABOVE** the law!

Relax, it's empty. Mustn't be being used by anyone.

How do *YOU* know? A tidy kid could have all their stuff in their backpack.

LOOK! It's still got my doodles!

Man, when they say PERMANENT PEN, they mean it.

I'd like to point out that drawing on a school locker is a **minor** offence.

Well, of course it was. I was a MINOR at the time.

And here's me as a MINER!

'MAGNO'?

Yeah, that's me as a **superhero.** I gave myself MAGNET POWERS!

The **MIGHTY MAGNO.**

Chapter 9

Soon...

I wonder ... Could a teacher from an *under-funded* department be stealing mascots in protest of school sports budgets?

If so, it's certainly not this shop teacher.

He's got more wood than a woodchuck could chuck!

If a woodchuck could chuck wood.

BBRING!

All right, children. Remember to unplug the power tools from the outlet by the light switch.

Not to put too fine a point on it, but I made a nice little birdhouse.

Okay, nothing fishy about the shop teacher.

Now to suss out the **home economics** teacher.

Settle down, students.

I see we have a new face in class.

GUNDERBOOT

FOOD DRIVE

If you haven't yet noticed, here at P.S. 366, **EGGS** are very important.

Our **mascot**, Bucky, is of course a big egg, which you'll all see at tomorrow's pep rally.

But more importantly, an egg represents growth...

...development...

...learning...

...AND THE FRAGILE NATURE OF LIFE ITSELF!

≥GASP!≤

flap flap flap

For an egg to survive it needs lots of **care** and **protection.**

But it mustn't be *CODDLED* from the crushing truths of the REAL WORLD!

Likewise, **education** is meant to prepare you for the facts of existence.

So your **homework** is to *lovingly nurture* an egg until Monday.

Boy! This teacher's really passionate about eggs . . .

WAIT — could they care about eggs SO MUCH that they would *STEAL* the mascot costume?

Oh, sorry. I'm one short.

You can, uh... grab an **expired soup can** or something from that old FOOD DRIVE bin.

Will they hatch?

No, these eggs are **unfertilized**. And no *cheating* by *boiling* them!

You must care for it as if it were your *OWN BABY!*

These **saltines** . . .

They're just like the ones my **former partner** became . . .

. . . when my failure to *save* him . . .

. . . turned him into **CRACKERDILE.**

I'm salty!

I wasn't able to save *YOU*, **Daryl** . . .

...BUT I **CAN** SAVE THESE CRACKERS!

OH! *Um* ...

⇒AHEM!⇐ I just have a very strong, er ... *maternal instinct.*

Now, for extra credit you can ...

Caring for you ... will be my **most important mission of all.**

Chapter 10

≥grumble≤

PRINCIPAL

Hm?

Phillip, I just got off the phone with your parents.

PRINCIPAL

Since neither of them can pick you up later, you will instead serve detention **first thing in the morning.**

One of them will drop you off an HOUR EARLY. Got that?

Baaaa, got it.

Something has to be done about your *BAAttitude.*

Now, hurry up or you'll miss the bus.

BRING

I've got TOO MANY things on my plate. The *last* thing I need is something ruining tomorrow's pep rally!

FINALLY, school's over.

Maybe now I'll be able to focus on the mission . . .

My cousin says he saw the **Valley High Viking** shopping at an outlet mall.

No way! I bet he just saw a REGULAR Viking.

Hmm . . . Did the **General Inspector** even *KNOW* about the mascots missing from the other schools?

Or has someone fed him misleading information to *lure* us here?

Maybe S.U.I.T. *HAS* been infiltrated by a **mole,** and we've been sent on some *WILD-GOOSE-EGG* chase!

Or *chicken egg,* I should say.

?

P.S. 366 PARENT/ TEACHER DAY NEXT THURSDAY

ACK! I never called **HOME!** And my calculator doesn't have cell service.

Hm . . . ?

BAA HA HA!!

You can't even *catch* my drift!

Hang on . . .

I've caught the **red rhino** AND the **blue tiger** . . .

Redwood Rhinos . . . Teal City Tigers . . .

AH-HA! *SEE,* Brash? I **have** been paying attention!

SHE must know something about the missing mascots!

I've got to . . .

BEFRIEND THAT SUSPICIOUS STUDENT!

If only there was a way I could do both **that** AND check up on my—

See ya on the **bus,** pigtails! ≤SNORT≤

The **BUS!** Of course.

You're no longer a scared kid, Mango. You're a *world-saving top secret agent!*

You got this.

HI! I AM NEW HERE!

Hello, New Here. I'm Nora.

HA! Heh heh. My name's—

Martin. I remember.

I hope that billygoat didn't get to you.

That kid gets EVERYBODY'S goat.

94

Then what could she have against school mascots? Against **Bucky?** A dislike of **foam** and **felt?**

An EGG ALLERGY???

inhale!

Splat

♪

⸗HURM⸗

What would Nora's motive be to steal the mascot costumes from every school in the district?

Chew, Chew

AH-HA!

That'll keep you safe and sound.

Now, let's get you out of this dank old boiler room.

Chapter 11

We're already at my old bus stop and I haven't got any **answers** outta this girl. I need more *time!*

Well, *er*, this is meeee . . . And, *uh* . . .

'EY! You gettin' out or what? I'd like to be rid of all you kids before dinner!

AH!

NORA, WOULD YOU LIKE TO COME OVER FOR—

Er, what's a good **kid food?** Caviar . . .? No. Cauliflower . . .? No! Brussels sprouts?!

Ooh, I KNOW!

— FISH STICKS?

OH! *Um,* sure.

Sounds better than getting spitballed by Phillip the rest of the way home.

PTOUiE!

And who can say no to a FISH STICK?

SCHOOL

This is my old—
I mean, CURRENT
house. Heh.

Cool. I'm just gonna text my
mum to let her know where I'll be.

OH! Could I . . .
borrow your phone
to text *MY* mum?

Tooooo . . .
let her know
I'm bringing a
friend over?

Aren't we right outside
your door? Why don't
you just knock?

I guess ya got me there.

Knock
Knock

We haven't seen you since—

THIS MORNING, WHEN I LEFT FOR SCHOOL!

But, Mango—

MUUUUUM, I told you not to call me that in front of my **FRIENDS,** *geez.*

What *should* your mother call you then, son?

Like, MY NAME.

...

IT'S MARTIN! DUH!

Don't 'DUH' your mother, **Martin**.

Is this a spy thing? Or a detective thing? What even IS your **job?**

Spies and **detectives** are _completely_ different careers—

MUM! I'M UNDERCOVER—

I mean, I'm under...covers! Because I'm...I'm...

...I'm reading so much for school...?

Hey!

You're not NEW HERE. You're OLD HERE!

That's not what it looks like! That was a, *um* ...Halloween costume...

Such a proud day.

Why'd you lie? Are there even any FISH STICKS here?

Oooh, are we having fish sticks for dinner?

You know you can't eat fried food. YOU'RE WATCHING YOUR SODIUM! We're having KALE SALAD and QUINOA!

Wait, please!

Before you go . . .

I just wanna know about the school mascots you captured!

Huh?

In class, you said you caught a red rhino and a blue tiger—

Oh, right! They're part of this **augmented reality** game.

A what now?

See? I hold up my phone . . .

...and I can see you've got an **Emerald Gator** right there.

Wait, sorry. That's your mum.

Hmm ... Just a *game*, you say. Really?

Well, *DUH!* It's called **Creature Capture GO!**

Your father hasn't been able to put it down.

I can stop playing whenever I want to.

OOH! You've got a rare **GOLDEN SILVERBACK** in your kitchen!

That's a silverback gorilla, but gold.

How did I miss *him?* He's worth a lot of **XP!**

It's very competitive, but it's not real.

Not ... real?

But what's this about missing mascots?

Are you some sort of **investigator?**

He's a **gator** who wears **vests.**

And *SOLVES CRIMES!* You always forget that part, Dad!

COOL BEANS

Uh, you wouldn't mind keeping my **under**cover identity **under** wraps, would ya?

Well . . . you don't have any **fish sticks.** *BUUUUT,* if you let **ME** capture that golden silverback, I'll consider it.

Dad . . . ?

COOL BEANS

Okay, *FIIIINE.*

DEAL!

COOL BEANS

Chapter 12

clack

Okay, I've confirmed Bucky's locker hasn't been tampered with. So our **mascot thief** hasn't struck yet.

If they're even after Bucky at all.

The pep rally is in less than twenty-four hours. Not enough time to look for clues at the other schools.

How has this culprit not been caught in the act?

If the **same person** showed up at each school, you'd think *eventually* a description of them would get out, and the *NEXT* school would know who to look for.

But I don't even know if they're **animal, vegetable** or **mineral!**

FACULTY

...and whatever you do, *DON'T* try Mr Gunderboot's **potato salad.** TRUST ME.

I gotta be here early to perfect my Bucky routine for the **PEP RALLY.** I end with this move called the *Double Benedict!* If I can't stick the landing, I'll *REALLY* have **egg** on my face. Heh heh! Get it?

Er . . . can't say that I do.

≤*Sniff*≥ WHEW! I think that potato salad wants revenge . . .

Unless you need anything else, I'm gonna head home.

Thanks again! You've been a **real dear.**

GO BUCKS!

Huh—?

What are you doin' lurkin' around the teachers' lounge?

Go on, kid.

Clear out before you get stuck in school overnight.

HEY, ease off! I've got a BABY!

Hmm ... The coach has a plausible **motive** ...

But he's TOO RECOGNIZABLE to have stolen the other school mascots.

At least ... not without an **ACCOMPLICE.**

Who to suspect when I'm suspecting ...

Maybe Mango's uncovered a co-conspirator.

Bop

Let's see, where is he ...

A few miles away. Did he wander off following something **shiny?**

Or did Mango follow a lead in the case ... into *DANGER?!*

LOCATE MANGO

vmm

115

AH-HA!

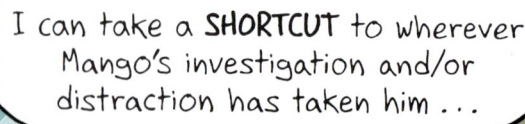

I can take a **SHORTCUT** to wherever Mango's investigation and/or distraction has taken him ...

WHAT WAS I THINKING?

I can't *flush myself down a toilet* with my *fragile defenceless child!*

Man, there are SO MANY THINGS I'm just not able to do anymore now that I'm a **PARENT!**

Chapter 13

Let me give you a ride home.

That's okay. I'm close enough to walk. Besides, there are some rare **creatures** nearby I want to **capture** on the way.

Get home safe!

See you in chem!

AAAH!!! HEY!

LEMME GO!

Did the **COACH** put you up to it? Steal the other school mascots to throw the teams off their **GAME???**

Mango! I just heard this kid say she was going to capture a **YELLOW-BELLIED WARBLER!**

She's after the mascot at Yellowville Yellomentary!

Put her down, Brish – *er,* BRIAN – *er,* **BRASH!**

She's just playing a PHONE game! It's all a **coincidence!**

Uh . . . really?

121

It's so wonderful that Mango's finally found a playmate.

≤Snore≥

Huh . . .? Where are my glasses?

Brash, welcome to my humble ab— **WHA—?!**

KEEP OUT

Hey, nice sewing machine.

That's my mum's! They've turned my room into STORAGE!

All that's left are my posters.

I MEAN – it's a **homework assignment.**

Speaking of homework, we'd better go over the **case!**

My lead turned out to be a **bust.**

What if ...*Hm.* Maybe ...Maybe kids at the different schools are DARING each other to steal the mascots?

Like a prank?

I wouldn't be surprised if this was all some viral **ClikClok** trend gone too far. As for that being a S.U.I.T. concern, we both know how *EXTREMELY ONLINE* the General Inspector can be when it comes to **social media.**

Kinda weird for a guy who is otherwise not very *tech-savvy!*

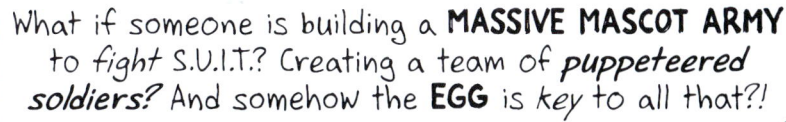

125

Chapter 14

Morning . . .

≥giggle≤

≥GASP!≤

Hmm?

HA HA HA HA HA HA

AAAAHHH!!!

AAAAAAHHH!!!

WHA—?!

What is it? Is the baby okay?

Oh... ⇒Whew!⇐ It was only a nightmare.

I dreamt I showed up to school NAKED!

Mango, you run around naked all the time.

Yeah, but without my V.E.S.T., it blew my COVER!

Being back in school brings out so much anxiety!

Knock Knock

Occupied!

Dad? Are you gonna be a while?

Son, you should know by now that there are *some* things in life you just can't *RUSH*.

CREATURE CAPTURED!

Bronze Bison, ooh!

MUUUUUUM! DAD'S TAKING TOO LONG!

Oh, he'll be in there for at *LEAST* forty-five minutes.

Come, I'll drive you to school. I packed you a lunch!

OH! It's *you* again.

Where's Mango? I mean, where's MARTIN?

He's travelling by, *um* ... **alternative** means of transportation.

Well, at least PHILLIP isn't on the bus.

Who? The **BULLYGOAT.** He always teases me when I get on.

He teases *everybody*, really.

Pushing, shoving, insults, name-calling...

He even has a vendetta against our mutual friend.

Has this Phillip kid *always* acted out like that?

For as long as I've known him.

But bullies aren't *BORN* that way, are they?

Like, something has to *MAKE* someone into a bully...right?

Well, Brash is overcompensating for leaving his former partner for dead in a vat of **radioactive saltine dough** that turned him into an evil monster called **Crackerdile**.

I'm sorry, what?

Oh, look, we're here.

Bye, Mum. Love you.

WAIT! YOU FORGOT YOUR LUNCHBOX!

IT'S GOT THAT CARTOON YOU LIKED ON IT! **CLAM CONTROL!**

It's **CLAW Control,** Mum.

I made your favourite. Honey, baloney and jalapeño with the crusts cut off!

Thank you, Mum.

§Tch!€ *Awww,* **whole wheat?**

THE EXTRA FIBRE IS GOOD FOR YOUR BOWELS!

EEK!

Can't let Burrowbridge see my face...

≋Whew!≋

Claw Control? *HA HA!* That show is for BABIES!

I meant this morning! We only have to keep the mascot costume safe for a few more hours till the **PEP RALLY.**

Oh, and then we'll *still* need to find the *OTHER* missing team mascots.

And we can't forget about the S.U.I.T. security threat!!!

And I'd better change *him* before class.

Just get to the gym already!

BRINNNG!

ARGH! If I had hair, I'd be PULLING IT OUT!

Chapter 15

See? This is what Daddy uses to investigate crime.

Morning, class! Sorry I'm late.

Gunderboot's **potato salad** is STILL workin' its way through me.

≳Phew!≲

COACH

Oh, no. I forgot to check—

BUCKY . . . ?

...and THAT is why **oil** and **water** don't mix.

This sub is actually a great teacher.

She really knows how to keep a student engaged!

OW! *HEY,* stop *kicking me.*

Huh?

TEACHER! **MARTIAN** KEEPS **KICKING ME!**

I AM NOT! He's lying!

Settle down or you'll *BOTH* be sent to the **principal's office.**

But . . . !

I'll get my **payback** by day's end. You can count on it.

You'll find out why they call me the **GOAT.**

Pretty sure I already know.

Attention, students and faculty. This is Principal Queens-Burrowbridge. Our dear mascot, **BUCKY** . . . has been **TAKEN.**

WHAT?!

To the **perpetrator** . . . I don't know *who* you are. I don't know *what* you want. If you are looking for **ransom** I can tell you the school doesn't have it in the budget.
If you return the costume now, that'll be the end of it. I will not *look* for you, I will not *pursue* you. But if you *DON'T,* I will **find you** and you will face **EGG*spulsion!***

Regardless, the **PEP RALLY** will *still* take place as scheduled.

Even if it will lack a certain... **pizzazz.**

≥TCH!≥ The pep rally is gonna be so *BOOORING* without Bucky!

OooOOOoh, whoever poached Bucky is gonna be in *HOT WATER!*

BAA ha ha ha!

Hilarious.

Right, MARTIAN?

≥SNORT≥

Here I was worried about school grades. I'm gonna get an **F** in **detective work!**

≥Sniff≥ Oh, EWW! Pee-yew, what *IS* that?

UH-OH!

Why do I smell **rotten eggs?**

I mean— OH! Someone forgot to tighten this container of **SULPHUR** . . .

Heh heh.

And **sulphur** smells . . . like . . . er . . . I swore I'd never do this as a substitute, but . . .

CLASS, it's time for a **VIDEO!**

YAY!!!

VCR

PLAY

PRESS!

EGGSCUSE me, kids . . .

I just need to pop out for a second.

click

149

Something about this doesn't smell right...

The very thing we were supposed to prevent, and it happened right under our **prominent noses!**

Speaking of *NOSES*, I should contact the **G.I.** so he *KNOWS* we fowled up.

But I can't do that here, and I can't ditch class...I don't have a **hall pass!**

There's gotta be a way to fix this. *Surely* the thief left a **clue** at the crime scene.

And Brash is already in the gym!

All we need is one **solid lead** and Brash and I will know *EGGsactly* who's behind this by lunchtime!

Chapter 16

But by lunchtime . . .

ALREADY?

Normally I'd love for a school day to fly by, but not when I'm conducting an investigation!

UGH, Phillip again . . .

It's a good thing I've got everything in my **B.A.C.K.pack.**

Hey! I guess I *AM* that tidy kid!

Walkin' away?

Whatsamatta? You **chicken?**

You can't *EGG*nore me forever, Martian!

Focus on the Martian, mission. *I mean—* DANG IT!

You have reached the **General Inspector.**

Just kidding! You've reached my **voicemail hologram!**

The *REAL* me is away from my desk at the moment, most likely doing covert S.U.I.T. duties. Or *S.U.I.T.ies!*

Perhaps I'm somewhere undercover. Or maybe I'm just in the bathroom.

For all *I* know, I could be climbing a mountain!

Which makes me wonder ...*WHY* is the General Inspector climbing a mountain?

That kid in the Bucky costume...

That's G.I. Moe!

The **GENERAL INSPECTOR!**

He *ALSO* went to this school?

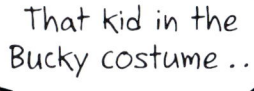

Someone *IS* digging into the **past** of a S.U.I.T. agent – the **General Inspector's** past!

Our culprit must have discovered G.I. Moe was a mascot performer as a child...

...but they *DIDN'T* find out what school he went to...

...so they've been systematically stealing mascots from EVERY SCHOOL hoping to narrow it down!

It's like Brash said — if a villain knows *ONE* detail about your past, imagine what **OTHER** secrets they could unlock with that information?

Somehow this villain will find a way to use that egg *against* the General Inspector.

I may have just **CRACKED** this case wide open!

It's not actually about **sports** at all — but I sure hope Brash has his *head in the game!*

Chapter 17

Principal Queens-Burrowbridge will be right back, Martin.

Sit here, and do NOT move.

But! But!

GREAT.

Ms Burrowbridge is probably gonna give me *detention for life!*

Just when I had a breakthrough in the case!

How do I explain being here without blowing my cover?

What's this?

How did Ms Burrowbridge get our new top secret S.U.I.T. ID photos?

≩GASP!≨ There is a **mole** after all . . .

Principal Queens-Burrowbridge is the mole! Both *literally* and *figuratively!*

MAURICE MAKES OUR MASCOT MOVE

Somehow she found out her former student grew up to become the head of a **covert spy organization.**

I should have known she was a criminal mastermind when she wouldn't give me extra credit for my periodic chemistry jokes!

Look! I made a **table of L-M-Ns!**

PERIODIC TABLE OF ELEMENTS

This isn't **shop class,** Mango.

165

Everyone's heading to the gym for the pep rally.

Stay Classy! *(Go to class!)*

LAB

Here we are.

Ah, a **microscope!** Perfect!

Let's take a closer look at **Junior,** here.

Hang on . . .

The **follicles** I found! Or folli**CLUES,** I should say.

I almost forgot about them!

166

Yesterday I was hard on Mango for not *focusing* on the case . . .

. . . and here *I* am, obsessing over a handful of **saltines** with a *one-in-a-million chance* of containing any remnant of **Daryl** . . .

Okay, one mission at a time.

Won't need the overhead projector . . .

Hmm, there's a couple of wiry, white, ORGANIC hairs . . .

But surely the egg costume is made of *INorganic* foam . . .

169

DUNP!

!

HOW THE—? Why would Ms Burrowbridge hide BUCKY in a locker?

≥GASP!≤ She knows this locker used to be MINE. She's TAUNTING me by stuffing this suit in here.

Well, I won't be intimidated . . .

I'll find a way to turn this evidence EGGainst HER!

And there's no better place to HATCH a plan . . .

UNZIP!

. . .than INSIDE AN EGG!

Now to locate Brash so we can expose this *MOLE mole* as the threat to our agency.

Geez, kids have written all over the inside of this thing.

'Moe hearts Burrowbridge'?

Did...the General Inspector... have a CRUSH on a TEACHER?

Yeesh, that's embarrassing.

Hold on. Could *THAT* be what this was about all along?

Is someone stealing mascot costumes to find childhood confessions that could be used to **blackmail** students who grew up to be people in positions of power???

Huh? Looks like Brash is in . . . the **BOILER ROOM?**

BRASH

P.S. 366 - FLOOR PLAN

≷*GASP!*≶ That's the scariest place on school grounds!

LOOK! BUCKY'S BEEN FOUND!

Where?

OH! Uh . . . *GO BUCKS!*

READ

HEY! The pep rally is *THAT* way!

buck
buck
buck
buck
buck
buck

Chapter 18

Hwuuu...Steam...?

No...NO! The **crackers**... They're getting all *mushy!*

FSH!

Who's there...? ≥*GASP!*≤ D-Daryl?!

PSH!

No. Just a foam costume...

CC CROCS

It's the Cook County Croc! And the **Teal City Tiger!** The **Valley High Viking!** The **Redwood Rhino!** And...

. . . the Fairville Fox?

The **SUBSTITUTE!** You're no **fox**, you're—

A **SKUNK.**

YOU stole the mascot costumes?

But *WHY?*

All I want to do is TEACH, but no one wants to hire a **skunk.**

Everyone thinks we *SMELL* all the time!

When in fact, skunks only *really* smell as a **defence mechanism.**

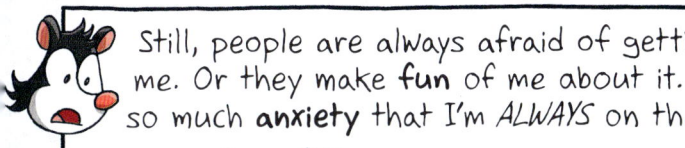

Still, people are always afraid of getting close to me. Or they make **fun** of me about it. It gives me so much **anxiety** that I'm *ALWAYS* on the **defensive.**

I've been wearing these school mascot costumes to *pretend* to be **different animals** and get jobs as a substitute teacher.

But I get so *NERVOUS* about being discovered that my defence mechanism inevitably *kicks in.* The foam is only able to fend off the funk for so long.

This tiger seems familiar . . .

Err . . .

poot

I couldn't afford fancy **industrial-strength dry-cleaning** on a part-time teacher's salary!

So I'd steal ANOTHER costume and move on to ANOTHER school.

But I've run out of schools! I've been trying to STEM— I mean, STEAM the smell out in this boiler room and hoping these **scented candles** will help mask the odour.

I assumed *THIS* school had a *DEER* mascot. The team's called the **BUCKS,** fer cryin' out loud!

So I swiped the coach's key . . .

But last night when I opened that equipment locker, **BUCKY** turned out to be a silly **EGG!**

I can't be a substitute in an *EGG COSTUME!*

Egg substitutes *NEVER* work! *Especially* in **baking recipes.**

So . . . if *YOU* don't have **Bucky** . . . who does?

176

177

clink

clank

SMUSH!

SHLURP!

The foam costume absorbs the soggy saltines like a sponge!

Ba...Ba...

...and long story short, I came across a **fax** saying there were undercover agents at the school. Your photos make you look like **FROGS,** by the way. Now that you're both here, I imagine you'll arrest me.

First things first. Mango, who *DID* take the egg? Do they have—

I *thought* I was hot on their tail, but now— *WAIT* . . . It's *MY* tail that's **hot!!!**

AAAAAAAAAAAAAAAAAAAAAAAHHHHHHHHHH

Stop, drop and egg roll!

Chapter 19

WHAT? NO! Don't cheer *him!* He **RUINED** the pep rally!

HE stole the mascot costume in the first place!

It was in his locker this whole time!

NO! I mean, *yes,* but— how'd YOU know that?

Because **HE** stole the egg!

And he tried to FRAME YOU as *retribution* for him getting **detention!**

Um . . . Nuh-uh!

Phillip was at school early for morning detention. The coach was running late. He noticed the **key** to the mascot storage cabinet was, er . . . left behind.

Uh. Hello?

Hmm . . .

Heh heh . . .

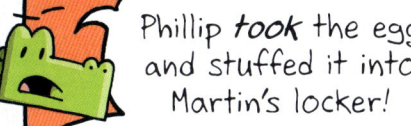
Phillip **took** the egg and stuffed it into Martin's locker!

Then he stood guard by it all day to scare Martin off from discovering it until it was time for the pep rally.

Hurr hurr...
≥SNORT≤

Once the pep rally was *ruined*, Phillip would make sure Martin took the fall.

You can't prove any of that!

But I can! The *THIEF* shed a **wiry white hair** at the scene of the crime. And it matches the hair *YOU* shed when you *wilfully dropped* my **cracker baby!**

Chapter 20

Soon . . .

. . . I've known forever that Maurice went on to become a **super sleuth.** We've kept in touch for years.

When I heard multiple school mascots had disappeared, I reached out to him. Your General Inspector was one of the *BEST* mascot performers to ever don Bucky.

Little Maurice *loved* wearing that **EGG SUIT.**

That's not *ALL* he loved.

He faxed over an ***entire dossier*** explaining his top agents would look into it.

He said I should act like business as usual.

Still not sure why he sent photos of **frogs,** though . . .

MANGO

BRAC

Well, we *failed* at saving your mascot. But at least the pep rally still got everyone *PUMPED* for the season!

And with Bucky in ashes, *NO ONE* will learn the G.I. had an **embarrassing crush** on you as a kid. *I mean*—

Oh? I had no idea! Maurice didn't have to go to such lengths for something as *innocent* as that.

And from so long ago!

It can be hard for some of us to get over the **insecurities** of our youth.

My dear Mango. If ever I was too hard on you, it was only because I wanted you to reach your **full potential**. I'm glad Maurice took my advice when I recommended you for his spy organization.

You did? *Awww*... Now I'm embarrassed for thinking you were a **mole**.

I mean a *mole*, not a **mole**. The other kind of *mole*. Well, both, really.

And *I'M* embarrassed for being responsible for so much of this.

I apologize. And now . . . my teaching days are over.

I'll of course return the mascot costumes, but . . . I don't know what to do about their smell.

Don't worry. I can guarantee those suits will be *thoroughly* LAUNDERED before being sent back.

I want you to know that your **teaching** *DOESN'T* stink, Ms Foxworth.

Thank you, Mango. I just . . . wish I had the **confidence** to teach without hiding my identity.

Also, my name's not really Foxworth. It's **Hyacinth**.

Hiya, Cynthia.

No, Hyacinth.

Isn't that what I said?

I'm here to pick you up— **MANGO!** *WHY* are you *NAKED?* You'll catch cold!

Mum?

You need at least *ONE* article of clothing on . . .

HERE! Your father always keeps a pair of **clean underwear** in the glove compartment!

Ew, Mum, *NO!* I am *NOT* putting those on!

OOOH, a rare **TIGHTY-WHITEY ALLEY-GATEY!**

Now *THAT'S* embarrassing.

Ms Hyacinth, I think I have a teaching opportunity for you. So long as you're willing to trade in wearing **mascot suits** . . . for *ANOTHER* type of **S.U.I.T.**

That sounds amazing!

But . . .

. . . what if I get nervous again and lose control of my *common scents?*

That won't be a problem.

191

Gettin' clean for our team way down, underground,
Wow, they're really gettin' in there!
DEEP SCRUB
SCRUB
SCRUB
SCRUB
SCRUB
There's a new S.U.I.T. instructor that we found!
COLD RINSE
PSSH
COMB!
It's been a while since I was treated to a spa day!

We want the SKUNK! Gotta have that SKUNK!
SPIN CYCLE
BBRBRBRBBBRBBRRRBBRBR
TWIRL!
OWW, here comes the skunk! Teacher's a skunk!
HOT PRESS
FFFSSSSSSSS
FFSSSSSSSSSSS
Ahhhh . . . I could get used to this!

Speaking of adjusting...

Those saltines came to life, Mango.

I believe you, Brash.

It means there are *MORE BOXES* of **Saul T. Byproducts radioactive crackers** out there... Some of which may even have a bit of my **former partner Daryl** in them!

We *HAVE* to track them down, or else ...*WHO KNOWS* what might happen?

SALTINES

InvestiGators! Where are you? Time to report in!

VMM

Come on, BRIAN.

We don't want to be *LATE!*

Epilogue

General Inspector, you said that mission was a matter of **S.U.I.T. security.** But really you just didn't want an *embarrassing* piece of your childhood getting out?

It's much more than that! My **two-factor security question** is 'Who was your favourite teacher?'

And if some villain knew the answer is **'Ms Burrowbridge,'** they'd be able to *STEAL MY IDENTITY!*

When I got wind of mysteriously missing mascots, I isolated myself in case someone was onto me.

Then I sent you two to make sure my secret wouldn't fall into the wrong hands and be used against me.

Why didn't you just *CHANGE* your security question?

I DON'T KNOW HOW! I need **Monocle** to do it!

Oh, for crying out loud. Surely you coulda *TOLD* Burrowbridge about it!

You mean confess that I had a schoolboy **crush** on her all those years ago? I'd be *MORTIFIED!*

Kids made fun of me for liking Ms Burrowbridge, so I'd deny it! But I found a place to express my truth inside that costume. In **permanent pen!**

...All right, friends, family and students of P.S. 366! Give it up fooooor...

...THE **BURN-IGATORS!**

Check out the hot new jerseys!

I guess an alligator named **BURNY** makes as much sense as an egg named **BUCKY.**

199

Special thanks to . . .

Wes Dzioba for his radiant colours.
My editors, Calista Brill and Dave Roman,
plus everyone at First Second and Macmillan.
Clare Hall-Craggs and the rest of the UK team.
My agent, Jen Linnan and Gina Gagliano,
for always being on top of things.
Pat Lewis, Christopher Hastings
and Steve Foxe, for going the extra mile.
Karen Grenke and librarians everywhere.
Teachers, substitutes, mascots
and substitute mascots.
And Susan Graham for being so nice to me.

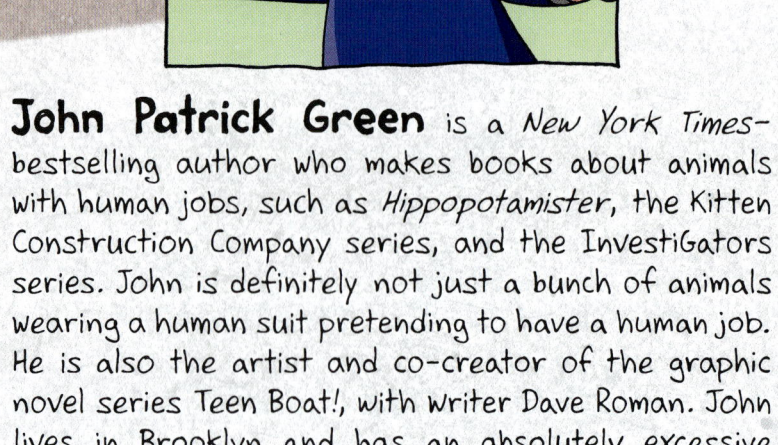

John Patrick Green is a *New York Times*-bestselling author who makes books about animals with human jobs, such as *Hippopotamister*, the Kitten Construction Company series, and the InvestiGators series. John is definitely not just a bunch of animals wearing a human suit pretending to have a human job. He is also the artist and co-creator of the graphic novel series Teen Boat!, with writer Dave Roman. John lives in Brooklyn and has an absolutely excessive amount of LEGO. Like, seriously. SO. MUCH. LEGO.